This Orchard book belongs to

_____

_____

_____

Ankylosaurus
an-ki-loh-sore-us

Iguanodon
ig-wah-noh-don

Triceratops
try-serra-tops

Brachiosaurus
brak-ee-oh-sore-us

Velociraptor
vel-oss-ee-rap-tor

Plesiosaurus
plee-see-oh-sore-us

Diplodocus
dip-lod-oh-kus

Oviraptor
oh-vee-rap-tor

Pteranodon
ter-an-oh-don

Stegosaurus
steg-oh-sore-us

Tyrannosaurus
tie-ran-oh-sore-us

For Peter — MM

For Henry, Elinor, Ollie and Milly — AA

ORCHARD BOOKS
First published in Great Britain in 2010 by Orchard Books
This edition first published in 2016 by The Watts Publishing Group
3 5 7 9 10 8 6 4
Text © Margaret Mayo, 2010
Illustrations © Alex Ayliffe, 2010
The moral rights of the author and illustrator have been asserted.
All rights reserved.
A CIP catalogue record for this book is available from the British Library.
ISBN 978 1 40834 929 8
Printed and bound in China

Orchard Books
An imprint of Hachette Children's Group
Part of The Watts Publishing Group Limited
Carmelite House
50 Victoria Embankment
London EC4Y 0DZ

An Hachette UK Company
www.hachette.co.uk
www.hachettechildrens.co.uk

Margaret Mayo & Alex Ayliffe

STOMP, DINOSAUR, STOMP!

ORCHARD

Mighty Tyrannosaurus

loved stomp, **stomp**, **stomping,**

Gigantic legs **striding,** enormous jaws **opening,**

Jagged teeth waiting for guzzle, **guzzling!**

So **stomp,** Tyrannosaurus, **stomp!**

Immense Diplodocus

loved swish, swish, swishing,

Long tail flicking and fast whip, whipping.

Enemy surprising and – **smack!** – scaring.

So **swish**, Diplodocus, **swish!**

Crested Pteranodon
loved glide, glide, gliding,
spreading **wide** wings, circling, **rising**,

Higher and **higher**, swooping and **soaring**.

So glide, Pteranodon, **glide!**

Fierce Velociraptor

loved hunt, **hunt, hunting,**

In fearsome packs running, **racing,**

Hooked claws ready for quick pouncing.

So hunt, velociraptor, hunt!

Sleek Plesiosaurus loved zoom, zoom, zooming,
Sturdy paddles swooshing, flapping,

Neck lunging, teeth showing – **snatch!** – fish trapping.

So **zoom**, Plesiosaurus, **zoom!**

Tough Ankylosaurus

loved whack, **whack**, **whacking**,

Tail-club **swinging**, battles winning,

While hiding safely under spikes and armour plating.

So **whack**, Ankylosaurus, **whack!**

Massive Brachiosaurus

loved gulp, gulp, gulping,

Leaves picking, mouth stuffing . . . no chewing! . . . **fast eating,**

Hungry, **hungry** giant . . . **more** food needing.

So gulp, Brachiosaurus, **gulp!**

Wrinkly Triceratops

loved charge, **charge**, **charging**,

Thumpety-thump! Huge feet **pounding**,

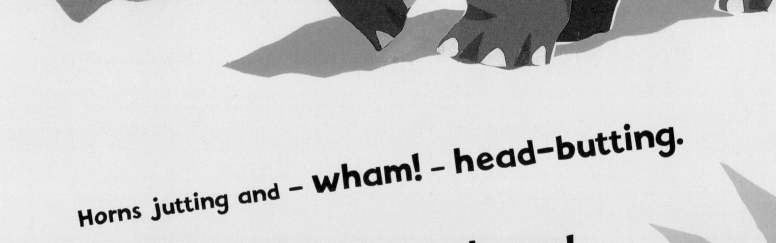

Horns jutting and – **wham!** – head-butting.

So **charge**, Triceratops, **charge!**

Stiff-tailed Iguanodon

loved chomp, chomp, chomping,

Tough plants grabbing, cutting and biting,

Chewing, mashing and noisy grinding.

So chomp, Iguanodon, chomp!

Feathered Oviraptor

loved guard, guard, guarding,

Soft sand shaping, snug nest making,

Eggs protecting, until – **cric-crac!** – babies **hatching.**

So guard, Oviraptor, **guard!**

Fantastic Stegosaurus

loved stroll, stroll, strolling,

Tiny eyes glaring, spiky tail waving,

Showing off big curvy plates . . . and looking quite **amazing!**

So stroll, Stegosaurus, **stroll!**

Imagine the creatures in a grand parade —

With no fighting allowed and no one afraid!

Some **plodding**, some **swooping** while others just **romp**,

And Tyrannosaurus leading . . .

STOMP! STOMP! STOMP!

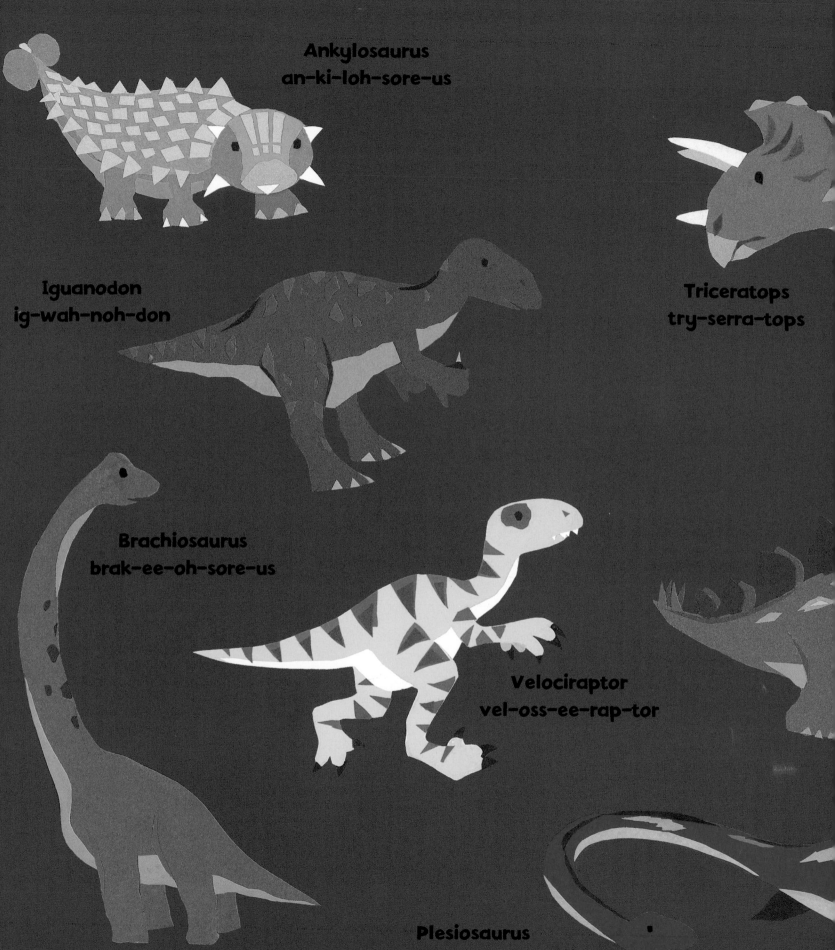

Ankylosaurus
an-ki-loh-sore-us

Triceratops
try-serra-tops

Iguanodon
ig-wah-noh-don

Brachiosaurus
brak-ee-oh-sore-us

Velociraptor
vel-oss-ee-rap-tor

Plesiosaurus
plee-see-oh-sore-us

Diplodocus
dip-lod-oh-kus

Oviraptor
oh-vee-rap-tor

Pteranodon
ter-an-oh-don

Stegosaurus
steg-oh-sore-us

Tyrannosaurus
tie-ran-oh-sore-us